Captain Carson
Goes to Bali

By: TeAndra and Carson Taylor

Illustrated By: Samayyah Smith

Authors Dedication:

This book is dedicated to my

great grandparents,

Virgil and Mary Toombs

Illustrators Dedication:

For Jai & Jaden

Hi, my name is Captain Carson, and I love to travel the world.

Traveling introduces you to new people, places and cultures.

Today were going on a trip to Bali.

Make sure to grab your passport, put on your straw hat and let's go on this adventure together.

Bali is the most visited island in the Indonesian archipelago.

An archipelago is a group of several islands.

It is only 8 degrees south of the equator.

Since it is so close to the equator, it can get really hot here.

There are so many activities that you can do in Bali.

You can pretend to be a baby bird sitting in a nest that overlooks the rice terraces,

or see Mount Anung, which is one of Indonesia's active volcanos!

Watch out for Lava!!

You can soar in the sky like Superman
on the Bali swings,

or catch some waves on one of Bali's beautiful beaches!

Surf's up dude!

Bali is the home to many animals.

At the Sacred Monkey Forest, there are
"Macaca" monkeys everywhere.

BEWARE!!!

Although they appear to be cute, they are very sneaky
and like to steal your toys, snacks
and even your favorite dinosaur backpack.

Another animal that is common to see in Bali, is the Elephant.

Let me hear your best elephant sound!

In many Asian countries, like Indonesia,
you can touch, feed and even
take a mud bath with an elephant.

Mud baths help to keep the elephant's
skin cool on hot days.

There are several beautiful temples in Bali.

Temples are sacred and peaceful
places for people to pray.

Some temples are in the middle of the ocean,
some are on top of mountains.

There's even a temple called Goa Gajah, which means "Elephant Cave."

Come on, let's go check it out!

Indonesia is a gorgeous country with so much culture and tradition to experience.

After all that fun, I think it's time to RELAX.

I really hope that you enjoyed our trip,
and maybe you can visit Indonesia
on your own one day.

See you on our next adventure!

Captain Carson

Bali, Indonesia

May 2019

Printed in Great Britain
by Amazon

55370727R00020